SCUM GUM

MOULDY MILK

SOUR SNAIL

THE TRASH PACK™

THE GROSS GANG IN YOUR GARBAGE!™

SCABOON

VUL-GORE

JOOSED

GIDDY SQUID

SPEWSTER

NOXIOUS BEE

THIS GROSS ANNUAL BELONGS TO

....

AND COMES WITH BIN LOADS OF DISGUSTING ACTIVITIES, COLOURING, PUZZLES AND QUIZZES TO DO – IF YOU DARE!

Distributed by D.C. Thomson Books Ltd.
Courier Buildings
2 Albert Square
Dundee
DD1 9QJ

ISBN 978-1-4723-1920-3

Printed in Italy

THE TRASH PACK

THE GROSS GANG IN YOUR GARBAGE!

Annual 2014

TRASH CAN NEWS

"ONCE YOU PICK UP THIS TRASH-TASTIC BOOK YOU WON'T WANT TO PUT IT DOWN – WELL, YOU WON'T BE ABLE TO, 'COS IT'LL PROBABLY BE STUCK TO YOUR HANDS WITH SOME FOUL GUNGE OOZING FROM THE PUTRID PAGES"

"BRILLIANTLY BARF-MAKING – NEVER HAS THERE BEEN SO MUCH REVOLTING RUBBISH IN ONE GRUBBY PUBLICATION! A MUST-HAVE TOILET READ (WELL, THE PAGES MIGHT COME IN HANDY IF YOU RUN OUT OF TOILET PAPER)!"

PIZZA

CRUDDY CONTENTS

WELCOME TO TRASH TOWN

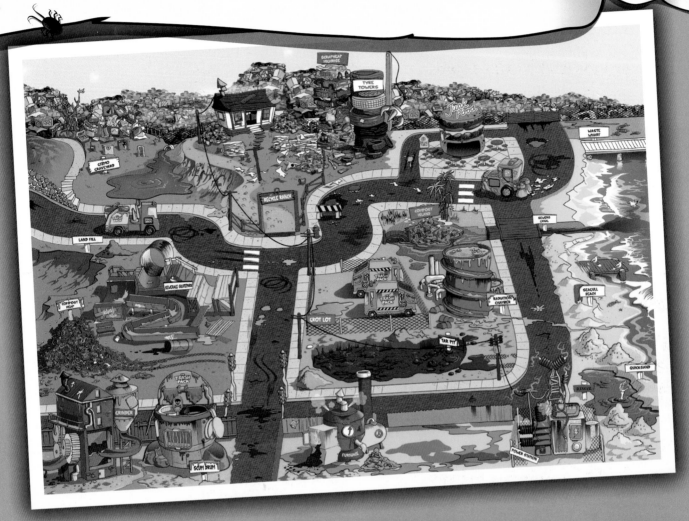

It's **GROSS, DIRTY, STINKY** and full of festering fungus and revolting rubbish. Once a thriving seaside town, Trash Town was overrun by nasty Litter Bugs who thoughtlessly tossed their trash wherever they roamed, and the rest is hideous history....

Out of all this stinky and manky mess, the **TRASHIES** evolved! These disgusting creatures are the stuff of your smelliest nightmares. They roam and slither in gross groups, spreading germs and gunge. Meet the Grubz, Bin-Sects, Bin Critters, Hard Rubbish, Bin Monsters and Movie Trash in the putrid pages of this foul-filled Annual.

*Lurking in a bin near you....
lift the lid if you dare!*

MEET THE GRUBZ

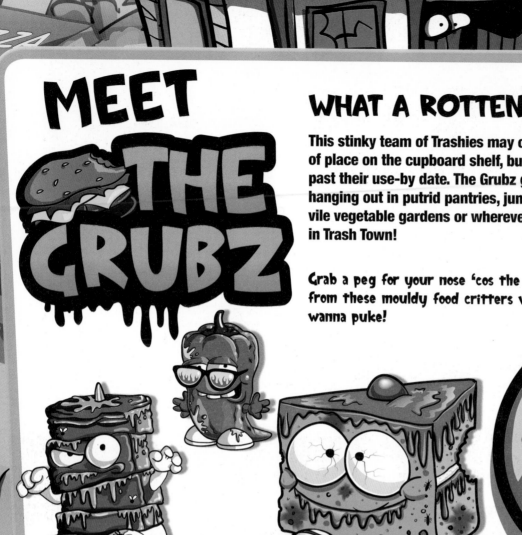

WHAT A ROTTEN BUNCH!

This stinky team of Trashies may once have had pride of place on the cupboard shelf, but now they are well past their use-by date. The Grubz gang can be found hanging out in putrid pantries, junk food restaurants, vile vegetable gardens or wherever there is a party in Trash Town!

Grab a peg for your nose 'cos the stench coming from these mouldy food critters will make you wanna puke!

WARNING: Always throw away the leftovers from your lunch box if you don't want to find one of these foul fellows festering in your school bag!

ENTER GRUBZ ZONE AT YOUR PERIL, CARRY A NOSE PEG AT ALL TIMES!

SHOCKOLI

ALWAYS EAT YOUR GREENS!

As boring as it sounds, adults are right when they say you must eat your greens. But even the strictest grown-up would forgive you for flinging this vile vegetable in the bin. Fuzzy with mould and oozing gunge, Shockoli is as shocking as his name suggests. He used to be fresh, but that was a *looong* time ago. 10/10 on the retch-monitor!

TRASH TOWN HANGOUT:
Vile vegetable gardens

8

SICK GARLIC

THE BESTEST AND UN-FRESHEST!

This is one stinky dude! Imagine the grossest, most grue-some garlic breath you can think of – that is how bad Sick Garlic smells. He stinks out every room he enters. You have to kind of feel sorry for him 'cos he can't help it, but nobody likes him. It's got to be bad if he has to hold his own nose!

TRASH TOWN HANGOUT:
Putrid pantries

MOULDY MILK

OLD, COLD AND FULL OF MOULD!

Hold your breath and cover your nose, 'cos this lumpy, creamy, putrid fellow has an out-of-this-world stinky stench that you would not believe! Mouldy Milk is a friendly guy who loves to hang out with cute kitties, but one swig of his foul contents will have you running to the toilet!

TRASH TOWN HANGOUT:
Feral fridges

SMELLY FISH

UN-FRESH IS BEST!

This gruesome Grubz's name says it all – he's extremely smelly and well…. he's fishy! If you can imagine the stink of old cat food, skunk breath and unwashed underarm hair all mixed up with sweaty socks, then you'll definitely know when you come across Smelly Fish!

TRASH TOWN HANGOUT:
Cruddy kitchens and Seagull Beach

WASTED BANANA'S WORDSEARCH

Have you checked the bottom of your school bag recently? That squishy oozing mess is probably Wasted Banana! Scrape him off this wordsearch and see if you can find the names of some of his grotty Grubz friends in the grid below.

It's enough to make you barf!

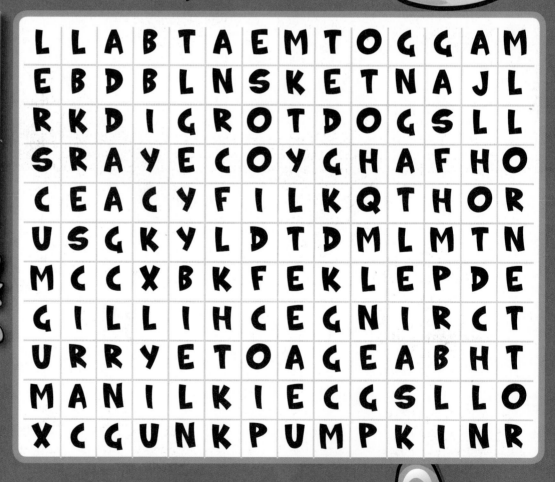

MAGGOT MEATBALL

CACKY CAKE

GUNK PUMPKIN

ROTTEN ROLL

CRINGE CHILLI

SCUM GUM

GROT DOG

L	L	A	B	T	A	E	M	T	O	G	G	A	M
E	B	D	B	L	N	S	K	E	T	N	A	J	L
R	K	D	I	G	R	O	T	D	O	G	S	L	L
S	R	A	Y	E	C	O	Y	G	H	A	F	H	O
C	E	A	C	Y	F	I	L	K	Q	T	H	O	R
U	S	G	K	Y	L	D	T	D	M	L	M	T	N
M	C	C	X	B	K	F	E	K	L	E	P	D	E
G	I	L	L	I	H	C	E	G	N	I	R	C	T
U	R	R	Y	E	T	O	A	G	E	A	B	H	T
M	A	N	I	L	K	I	E	C	G	S	L	L	O
X	C	G	U	N	K	P	U	M	P	K	I	N	R

SHOCKOLI'S SHADY SHADOWS

That vile vegetable, Shockoli, and some of his grimy Grubz mates, are hanging out in the kitchen of the Junk Food Restaurant. Their SLIMY SHADOWS are lurking in damp corners and musty cupboards. Can you match each Trashie to its shadow?

MEET THE BIN-SECTS

THEY'RE ENOUGH TO MAKE YOUR SKIN CRAWL – URRRGH!

If you come across a Trashie that's got six or more legs, and it's gooey and gross, then you've found a Bin-Sect. These creepy critters scurry, slither and slime their way around your home, lurking in dark corners! Just thinking about them will make you itch and scratch!

The Bin-Sects gang can be found hanging out in festering fruit bowls, under crumbs of food and grains of sand, hiding in your sheets, grazing the putrid paddocks of Trash Town or wherever it is dark and dank.

WARNING: You are never far from a Bin-Sect. Arm yourself with a fly swat or a can of spray repellent!

ENTER THE BIN-SECTS ZONE WITH CAUTION. YOU NEVER KNOW WHERE ONE OF THESE CRITTERS MIGHT BE LURKING! THERE'S NO ESCAPE!

PESTY PARASITE

THE TITCH THAT GIVES YOU AN ITCH!

Pesty by name and pesty by nature! This Trashie will definitely make the top 10 Pest List – and you won't be able to stop scratching if he is anywhere near you. That irritating itch on your scalp, those pus-oozing sores and lumps all over your body ... Pesty Parasite has been hard at work feasting on your tasty flesh!

TRASH TOWN HANGOUT:
Wherever it is dark and dank

WASTE WORM

THE WORM THAT MAKES YOUR STOMACH CHURN!

He's wiggly, he's squiggly, he's one squelchy worm! Next time you are having salad for lunch, make sure you check under those lettuce leaves, 'cos Waste Worm loves to snuggle up in their luscious green folds, leaving a trail of slime and ooze. The last thing you want is a mouthful of salad and rotten worm guts!

TRASH TOWN HANGOUT:
Inside old apple cores

SOUR SNAIL

IT'S SLIME TIME!

He's definitely not a delicacy that you'd like to have on your plate in a fancy French restaurant. This snail will only leave a sour taste in your mouth and have you retching into your serviette. Just be careful you don't step on him – he's a devil to scrape off your shoe!

TRASH TOWN HANGOUT:
Slimy streets and alleys

BLOW FLY

THERE'S A FLY IN MY GOOP!

This terrible Trashie will drive you nuts, buzzing around your head all day, and then vomiting his gross guts up all over your food. When he's not terrorizing you, Blow Fly loves nothing better than lazing around with his mucky mates in a nice, hot, steaming dog poo!

TRASH TOWN HANGOUT:
Everywhere there is trash and poo

TRASH-A-PILLAR'S CREEPY, CRAWLY CODE BREAKER

Trash-a-Pillar has left his putrid Bin-Sect buddies, a slimy secret note in a trail of rotten rubbish down at the compost heap. Use the CROSS ALPHABET CODE below to work out the message. Once you have solved the puzzle, why not try using the gruesome code to write your own messages for your mates.

SLUDGE SLUG'S MANKY MATHS

Sludge Slug may be slow, but when it comes to sorting and counting up rubbish, he's ONE SMART GUY! Dust out the cobwebs from your brain, then see if you can work your way through these manky trash maths problems.

1

BLOB MOZ collected 15 smelly salami. Grotty Bot Fly ate 5 of them, but then puked 2 back up. How many scummy salami are there now?

Answer

2

+

Answer

3

FERAL FLY spied 18 disgusting dog poos in the park. If he shares them with 6 of his foul friends, how many poos will they each have?

Answer

4

TRASHANTULA divided his bubonic burger into 4 equal parts. What percentage of the whole burger is each part?

6

SLUDGE SLUG took 2 hours to get from the compost heap to the sewers canal. How many mucky minutes is that?

Answer

5

ROCK ROACH has found 33 stinky old shoes. If he puts them into pairs, how many will be left over?

Answer

15

MEET THE

LURKING BY A RUBBISH BIN NEAR YOU!

These stinky critters spend hours rummaging through your rubbish bin. They can't wait to get their crusty claws on it so that they can eat it, or just keep it! The Bin Critters gang can be found grazing in putrid paddocks, swimming around in puke pools or wading in slime pits. They can also be seen wobbling on dangerously high power lines or statues.

Just follow the smell (if you can stand the stench, of course) ....

WARNING: Bin Critters will throw your rubbish all over the place, no matter how tight you tie up your rubbish bags!

ENTER THE BIN CRITTERS ZONE AT YOUR OWN RISK. WHERE THERE'S RUBBISH THERE'S ALWAYS A BIN CRITTER NEARBY, WAITING TO POUNCE.

TRASH RAT

NEVER LEAVE THE SEWERS WITHOUT YOUR GPS!

Top dog (or should that be rat!) of the litter pickers, Trash Rat is an expert when it comes to locating festering rubbish. He has a unique GPS (Garbage Pick-up System) that can pinpoint the exact spots where these terrible treats can be found. His meal of choice – decomposing nappies and fresh fish guts!

TRASH TOWN HANGOUT:
Drainpipes and sewers

VUL-GORE

FLYING FILTH!

Is it a bird? Well … kind of. Is it a plane? No … it's Trash Town's very own fungal fiend, Vul-Gore! This grotty creature of prey circles the skies above Trash Town, scouring the streets for stinky scraps. Vul-Gore isn't fussy when it comes to his festering food. This vulgar Trashie especially loves his dinner covered in maggot juice and cockroach poo! Barf-tastic!

TRASH TOWN HANGOUT:
High in the skies above Trash Town

SLIME PYTHON

THE SSSSSCCCCCCCC-UMMIER THE BETTER!

Slime Python is one sssslippery character! Sssplattered with sssstinking sssslime, he sssslithers his way through Trash Town, searching for filth to devour. No trash is too big for this putrid python. His jaws can open ssssssssoooooo wide he can ssssssswallow a whole tyre – even if it is still attached to the car!

TRASH TOWN HANGOUT:
Slime pits

SKABBY SHARK

GET HOOKED ON TRASH PACK!

If you're brave enough to take a dip in the Oozy Ocean, then watch out for a festering fin coming towards you through the murky waters. It will be Skabby Shark – he's back in Trash Town's wretched wet places, skulking through stinking sewage to find the most putrid bins to sink his teeth into.

TRASH TOWN HANGOUT:
Oozy Ocean and sewage

GROTWEILER'S CRUDDY CROSSWORD

Grotweiler loves rubbish. He's been patrolling the compounds of Trash Town and has collected a STINKING heap of rubbish. Solve the clues in this cruddy crossword to see what vile things he has found.

ACROSS:

1. A type of paper that has a disgusting wiping job to do!
4. Heading for a slimy slip!
7. Lots of smelly sardines are squashed inside this.
8. If it didn't stink like rotten cheese then you might want to find its matching pair!
9. Often found lying around at the Gizmo Graveyard, this rubbery thing once rolled along in Trash Town.

DOWN:

2. There's something fishy going on around here. What is that disgusting smell?
3. Would you like these fried, or scrambled? Or you could throw them at the nasty litter bugs!
4. Pop over to your local Junk Food joint to grab one of these meaty treats. Hope it doesn't make you barf!
5. Pooey! Grab a peg for your nose, and just remember not to throw the baby out with this piece of revolting rubbish!
6. If your teeth rot and fall out, you'll need some of these!

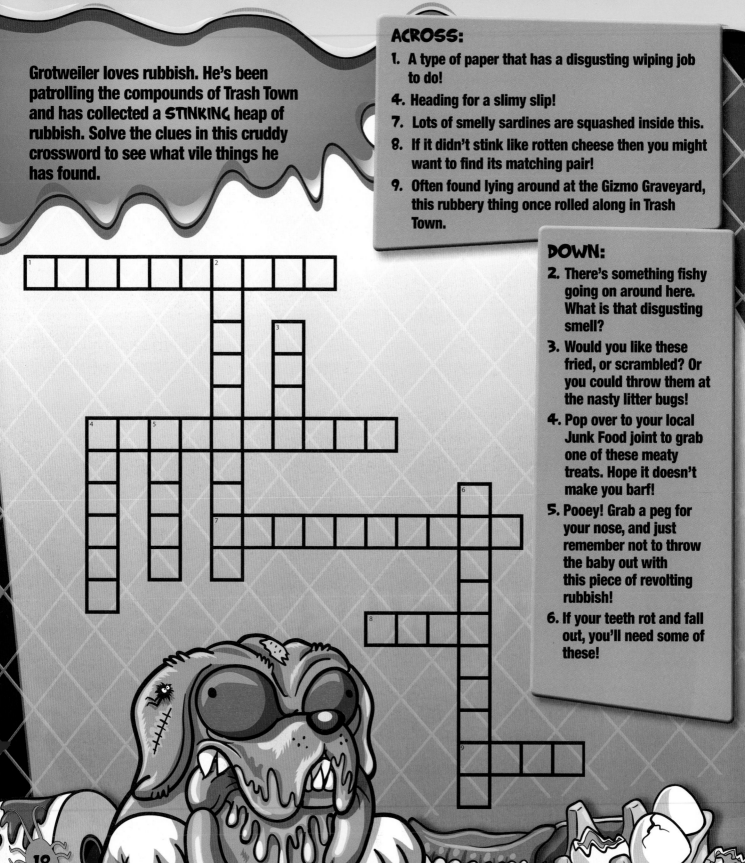

18

SKABBY SHARK'S AWFUL ANAGRAMS

Skabby Shark loves nothing better than swimming around in sewage and biting into bins to feast on their FERAL FLAVOURS! Unscramble the letters in each of the names below to find out which Bin Critter buddies this freaky fish is meeting for a foul food fiesta on Seagull Beach.

1. BAOSCON

2. YIGPG NIPEGO

3. SUOIXON EEB

4. MILES TOYHPN

5. BAGGARE TOGA

19

MEET THE HARD RUBBISH

HARDCORE TRASH!

You know all that broken stuff that piles up around your home – mangled TVs, ancient stereos, manky old sofas – yes, that grisly collection of unwanted guff really is hardcore rubbish. The front lawn is not the place to display it, unless you want a visit from the Hard Rubbish gang. These guys lurk wherever there is hardcore rubbish – in back and front gardens, in cruddy kitchens, around your home or down at the Gizmo Graveyard....

You can even find them lurking on displays in fine art establishments!

WARNING:
Take a trip to your local dump or recycling centre NOW, otherwise you're at risk of aiding and abetting members of the Hard Rubbish gang in your own home!

ENTER THE HARD RUBBISH ZONE WITH CARE, 'COS YOU'RE MORE THAN LIKELY GOING TO TRIP OVER A PILE OF TRASHED TOASTERS!

FOUL FISH BOWL

FOUL AND FISHY!

When you stop gagging from the swampy stench, you might want to feel a little bit sorry for Foul Fish Bowl, 'cos it's been years since anyone has changed his water. It's not really his fault that he's a terrible, manky tank of algae!

TRASH TOWN HANGOUT:
Lazing around lounge rooms

JUNK MAIL

YOU'VE GOT STALE MAIL!

This battered piece of junk is always stuffed full of unwanted bills, putrid pamphlets and contaminated catalogues. If you dare to turn the key in his lock and open his rusty door, he'll spew out a mountain of manky mail.

TRASH TOWN HANGOUT:
Gunky gardens

SEPTIX

SMELL YOU LATER!

Warning: Inspect carefully before sitting down! One sniff of this septic fella will have you running for the bathroom – but not the one where he lives! Arm yourself with a large bottle of disinfectant and your sense of toilet humour, 'cos stinky Septix loves telling jokes – the pongier and runnier, the funnier!

TRASH TOWN HANGOUT:
Barf-making bathrooms

FERAL FRIDGE

COOL AND CRUDDY!

You'd better have a strong stomach if you are going to open the door of this filthy fright! The skanky shelves in Feral Fridge are stacked full of fetid food that's old, cold and covered in mould! If you don't want to spend the night in hospital, DO NOT eat the frozen filth inside Feral Fridge – it'll leave you heaving!

TRASH TOWN HANGOUT:
Rotten restaurants

21

DISGUSTING DOT-TO-DOT

If Grot Pot offers you a cup of tea, politely say NO! One sip of the foul brew will have you running to the toilet. Join the dots to see him in all his steamy, sludgy glory! Then colour the picture with your grimiest colours.

PIZZA

OILY OINTMENT'S ODD TRASHIE OUT

Oozing with grimy grease, Oily Ointment can usually be found lurking around the flat tyres and old car parts in the Gizmo Graveyard. One of the pictures below is different from the others. Can you spot it before Oily Ointment squirts you with some GREASY GUNGE!

MEET THE BIN MONSTERS

SKULKING IN THE SHADOWS!

In the dark, dank alleys of Trash Town lurk the most hideous monsters of the Trash Pack – the mutant Bin Monsters. These mangled, manky critters are the ugliest brutes in the junk yard. If you want to find them (and it's unlikely), the Bin Monster gang can be spotted in the garbage truck parking lot, in sloppy sewers, and in old tissues.

They can also be found in Trash Lake, or swimming in drums of scum and generally wafting around Trash Town.

WARNING: If you see one of these grotesque creatures.... RUN! And don't look back!

ENTER THE BIN MONSTERS' ZONE AT YOUR PERIL. THE MAKERS OF THIS ANNUAL CANNOT BE HELD RESPONSIBLE FOR THEIR ACTIONS!

SPEWSTER

BIN-FULLS OF BARF!

Spewster is one of the sickest, smelliest Trashies in Trash Town – be careful you don't step in his vile bile! He oozes around town in a pool of steaming vomit full of carrots, peas, corn and whatever else was dinner last night!

TRASH TOWN HANGOUT:

Street corners, dark alleys and outside junk food restaurants

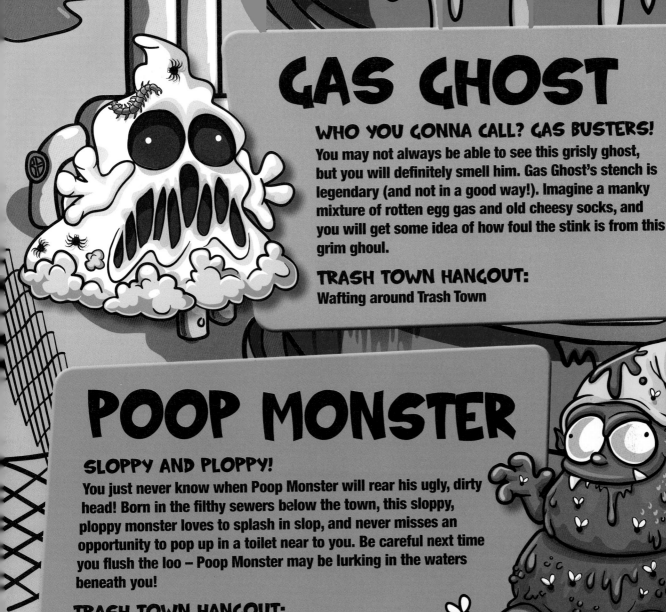

GAS GHOST

WHO YOU GONNA CALL? GAS BUSTERS!

You may not always be able to see this grisly ghost, but you will definitely smell him. Gas Ghost's stench is legendary (and not in a good way!). Imagine a manky mixture of rotten egg gas and old cheesy socks, and you will get some idea of how foul the stink is from this grim ghoul.

TRASH TOWN HANGOUT:
Wafting around Trash Town

POOP MONSTER

SLOPPY AND PLOPPY!

You just never know when Poop Monster will rear his ugly, dirty head! Born in the filthy sewers below the town, this sloppy, ploppy monster loves to splash in slop, and never misses an opportunity to pop up in a toilet near to you. Be careful next time you flush the loo – Poop Monster may be lurking in the waters beneath you!

TRASH TOWN HANGOUT:
Sloppy sewers

JOOSED

TRASH-A-LICIOUS!

He's sticky, icky, oozey and gooey! This gungy, gross critter is made up of all that disgusting stuff you find in the bottom of your rubbish bin. Joosed will slip and slide everywhere if you're not careful – his slimy speciality is leaking all over your feet when you take the bin out at night, and oozing between your toes – YUCK!

TRASH TOWN HANGOUT:
At the bottom of the bin

25

POOP MONSTER'S PLOPPY COLOUR COPY

Next time you go to the toilet, watch out for Poop Monster! You'll find him lurking in the ploppy, murky waters in the toilet bowl. If you have the stomach for it, copy the picture of this PUTRID POO using the grid on the page below.

27

MEET THE

LIGHTS, CAMERA, ACTION!

Meet the Movie Trash, the new stars of Trash Town! This motley crew are an icky, sticky selection of sweets, drinks and snacks that get stuck to your cinema seat or the bottom of your shoes! Tempting when fresh – but boy, can they turn your stomach when they have been festering in the filth and fluff of that stained cinema seat!

The Movie Trash gang can be found in all good junk food joints, sweet stores and cinema foyers ... and spilling from trash bags all over Trash Town.

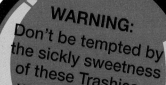

WARNING: Don't be tempted by the sickly sweetness of these Trashies – you don't want to miss the movie 'cos you're barfing up.

ENTER THE MOVIE TRASH ZONE WITH CAUTION. THESE MUCKY MOVIE MATES CAN STICK TO YOU LIKE GLUE!

POO-TATO CHIPS

THE CRISP THAT'S GONE AMISS!
Once crunchy and salty, Poo-tato Chips is now just a bag of soggy, stale old baked potato slices, that taste like they've been grabbed from the bottom of a compost heap! At least the pongy packet can double up as a barf bag!

TRASH TOWN HANGOUT:
In trash bags

ROTTY POP

STOP WHEN YOU POP!

This rotten movie treat may try to fool you with his hot butter or caramel coating, but one bite of his chewy pieces, and no amount of flavouring can disguise his disgusting taste! Not only does he leave a nasty taste in your mouth – he will wedge himself between your teeth, and have you speed dialling your dentist!

TRASH TOWN HANGOUT:
Cinema rubbish bins

BURPY SLURPY

TRASH IS SO COOL!

This fizzy, fungal Trashie might keep you cool on a hot day, but his sickeningly cruddy contents are more likely to give you a horrendous brain freeze and sugar rush. One sip of his fake flavours, and you'll be running to the bathroom!

TRASH TOWN HANGOUT:
Junk food shops

TRASHY TORCH

LIGHT OF YOUR LIFE!

He might be trashy and a bit cracked, but this little fella is actually a helpful chap. He will light the way to your seat and help you spot his gunky Movie Trash mates festering underneath it! Trashy Torch is one piece of rubbish you might actually want to take home with you!

TRASH TOWN HANGOUT:
Lighting up the shadows of Trash Town

SICKY, STINKY SEARCH AND FIND

The nasty litter bugs have been in Trash Town again – look at all this REVOLTING RUBBISH! If you're brave enough to sift through all this festering foulness before you pass out from the stench, then grab your protective gloves and get searching for all the trash featured on this page. Can you spot the six star Movie Trashies as well?

ROTTY POP   TRASHY TORCH   GROTTY COFFEE   BURPY SLURPY   POO-TATO CHIPS   SICKLY SWEETS

PIZZA   BROKEN PHONE   FILM REEL   BURRITO   GUM SPLAT   ICE CREAM

TRASHIE TRUE OR FALSE?

1. MOULDY OLD SHOCKOLI IS ONE OF THE PUTRID BIN CRITTERS.
   TRUE OR FALSE?

2. A LOT OF HARD RUBBISH ENDS UP IN TRASH TOWN'S GIZMO GRAVEYARD.
   TRUE OR FALSE?

3. SPEWSTER IS A BIN MONSTER WHO OOZES AROUND TRASH TOWN IN A POOL OF VOMIT.
   TRUE OR FALSE?

4. IF YOU DARE TO TAKE A SIP OF GROTTY COFFEE YOU WILL GET A BRAIN FREEZE.
   TRUE OR FALSE?

5. POOP MONSTER LURKS IN DARK, DANK CORNERS OF CRUDDY KITCHENS ALL OVER TRASH TOWN.
   TRUE OR FALSE?

6. TRASH-A-PILLAR HAS DREAMS THAT ONE DAY HE WILL TURN INTO A BEAUTIFUL BUTTERFLY.
   TRUE OR FALSE?

7. SICK GARLIC SMELLS SO WONDERFUL AND EVERYONE LOVES HIM!
   TRUE OR FALSE?

8. BUZZZZ! WHAT FLYING CRITTER LOVES LAZING AROUND IN STEAMING DOG POO? YES, IT'S BLOW FLY!
   TRUE OR FALSE?

9. AFTER A LONG, HARD DAY OF CLEANING UP TRASH IN TRASH TOWN, THE GARBAGE TRUCKS PARK UP IN THE TRASH TOWN COMPOST HEAP.
   TRUE OR FALSE?

10. WHEN SKABBY SHARK ISN'T FEASTING ON TRASH CANS, HE SPENDS HIS TIME SWIMMING AROUND IN CRUSTY OLD CUSTARD.
    TRUE OR FALSE?

SLIMY SPOT THE DIFFERENCE

They may be the stars of Trash Town, but the Movie Trashies are a SLIMY BUNCH. Littering a cinema near you, these gooey guys stick to your seat or the bottom of your shoe, or clog up the crevices in your teeth. Look at these two pictures of the Movie Trash crew and find 10 differences between them.

33

PUS POP'S PIMPLY PATHS PUZZLE

When you pop your pimples have you ever wondered where all that yucky YELLOW PUS goes? Well, somehow, it forms into a lumpy, gross ball of badness called Pus Plop! Pus Plop needs lots of sickly sweets and greasy junk food to keep him alive. Which putrid path should he follow to find his FOUL FEAST?

ROCK ROACH'S ROTTEN RIDDLES

RIDDLE ONE
What he lacks in size, this angry fella more than makes up for with his B-A-D attitude. If there's trouble in Trash Town, then this Bin-Sect is sure to be at the centre of it. Just be careful that you don't step on him – getting squished is his greatest fear.

RIDDLE TWO
This ugly creature is the stuff of hideous NIGHTMARES. If this Trashie decides to hide under your sheets, you can forget having a good night's sleep. His bites will leave you itching for weeks!

RIDDLE THREE
Look no further than that festering fruit bowl on your table. It is here that you will find this flying creature feasting on foul fruit. This buzzing Trashie will leave you an extra 'treat' – mini maggots wiggling all over the putrid fruit mush. TRULY GROSS!

RADIATION CHAMBER

35

STINKY SUDOKU

PHEWEE! Are you up for a stinky challenge? Grab a peg for your nose, and a pen to finish this putrid picture Sudoku puzzle by filling in the blank squares with the correct piece of garbage. Remember, each of the six bits of old rubbish must only appear once on each horizontal and vertical line, and each 6 x 6 box.

TAKE OUT THE TRASH!

HOW GROSS CAN YOU GET?
Design your own terrible Trashie for your bedroom wall.
Use the Trashies on the page opposite for inspiration!

IT'S A GARBAGE COLLECTION!

Write your name on this TRASH-TASTIC door hanger and ask an adult to help you cut it out. How disgustingly messy is your room?

DISGUSTING DOOR HANGER

THE GROSSEST WITH THE MOSTEST!

'S

REVOLTING ROOM!
ENTER THIS TRASH ZONE
(IF YOU DARE!)

DISGUSTING DOOR HANGER

TAKE OUT THE TRASH!

_____ 'S

RUBBISH ROOM! KEEP OUT! (BUSY MAKING A MESS)

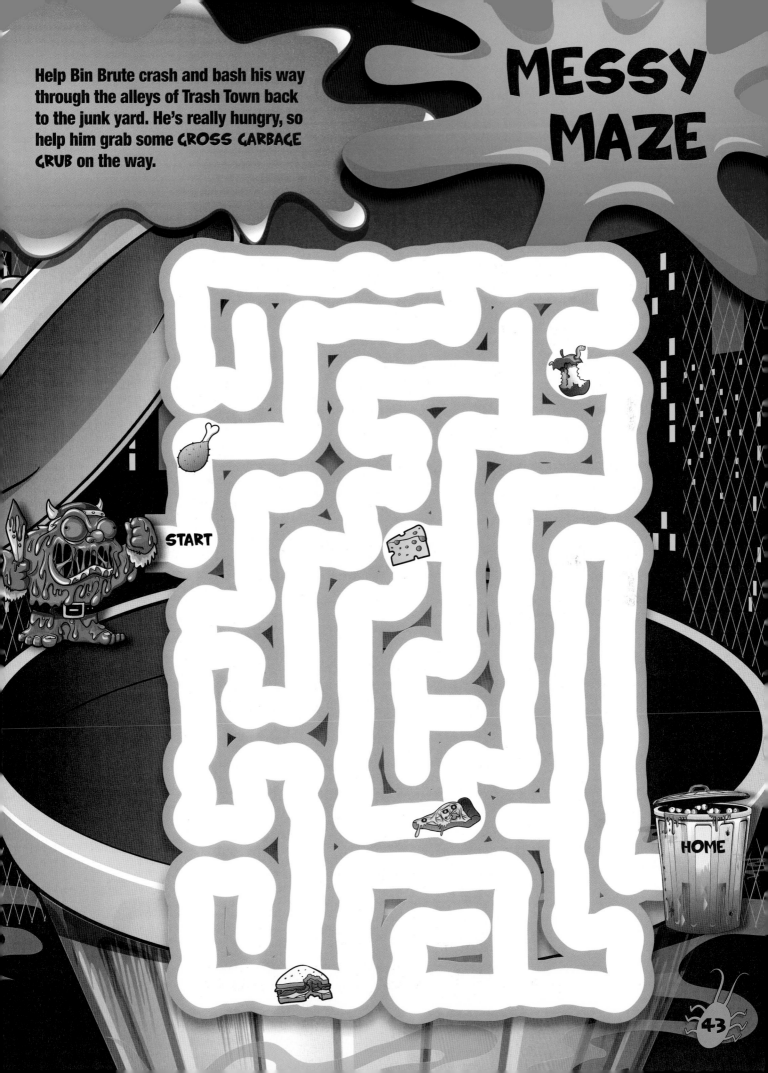

Help Bin Brute crash and bash his way through the alleys of Trash Town back to the junk yard. He's really hungry, so help him grab some GROSS GARBAGE GRUB on the way.

MESSY MAZE

START

HOME

43

WASTE WORM'S WORDSEARCH

Before you bite into that crunchy salad, you might want to check out this wordsearch puzzle to find out what CRUDDY CREATURES might be lurking there.

```
B L O B M O Z P T O G
E B D B W N S K E T N
R K D I A P L A F R L
M Y A Y S D O P G A T
A L A C T F A L K S G
A F G K E E D N D H U
L T C X W L F E T A L
U O L L O I C E G P S
T B T Y R A O T G I E
N Y N T M N N E C L G
A T L U E S P U M L D
H T T F H R O A G A U
S O R S W U D A G R L
A R A Y E O O U G E S
R G R Y E S L A M E A
T R R Y E T O B G R A
S K E L L Y S I C K L
```

BLOW FLY
SOUR SNAIL
TRASH-A-PILLAR
SLUDGE SLUG
WASTE WORM
BAD-ANT
BLOB MOZ
TRASHANTULA
GROTTY BOT FLY

PUTRID PATTERNS

Test your powers of observation and finish these putrid patterns by filling in the missing rubbish in each row. You'll need a **STRONG STOMACH**, because the stench coming off this rotten pile of rubbish is enough to make you puke!

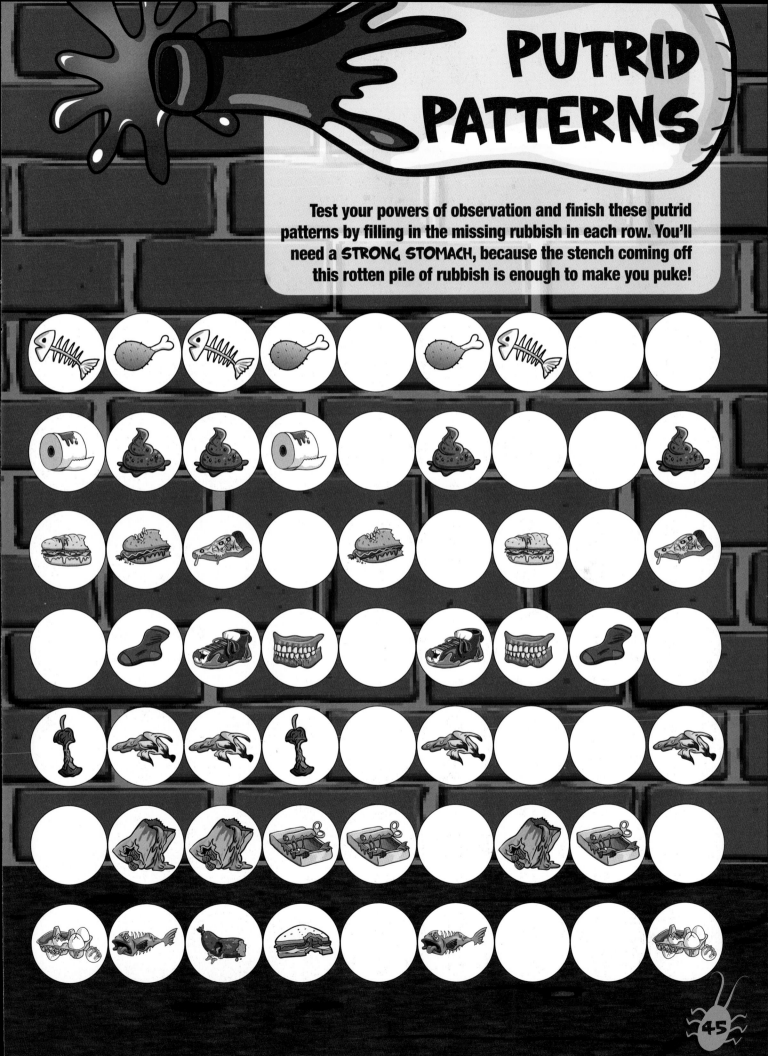

VUL-GORE'S WHO'S WHO?

While Vul-Gore was circling the stinky skies above Trash Town he spotted some of his TERRIBLE TRASHIE FRIENDS hiding amongst all the piles of rubbish on the streets. Look at these gross pictures and see if you can see which disgusting Trashies Vul-Gore found.

A

You've got stale mail! This Trashie is full of bad news and is always stuffed with unwanted bills.

....

B

She leaves a terrible trail of dripping drool wherever she goes. Hardly ever seen, this Trashie lurks in the deep, dark waters of Trash Lake.

....

C

You'll definitely get feral food poisoning from any festering food that this outdoor 'chef' cooks up.

....

D

This crusty critter has the longest, tackiest tentacles in Trash Town, and he loves to use them to grab the soggiest, grossest rubbish he can find.

....

KRUDDY KEBAB'S CRUSTY COUNTING

Kruddy Kebab was once juicy and tender. Now he's as tough as an old boot, with a CRUSTY, SCABBY SKIN. Overcooked and grouchy from spinning on a spit day and night, Kruddy Kebab can only dream of being a different piece of junk food…! Sigh! How many chicken drumsticks can you see in Kruddy Kebab's dream?

Answer

Do you know your Grubz from your Bin-Sects, the Gizmo Graveyard from the compost heap? Test how grubby your garbage knowledge is by taking this grotesque Trashie quiz.

8 YOU'LL NEED A SICK BUCKET IF YOU PUT THIS GUNKY GUY ON YOUR GROT DOG OR SHAM-BURGER.

9 WHO IS THE JOKER OF THE TRASH PACK?

10 YOU DEFINITELY DON'T WANT THIS JUICY TRASHIE TO BE LURKING IN YOUR CRISP SALAD. WHO IS HE?

11 WHAT SLIPPERY, SLIMY CRITTER CAN OPEN HIS OOZING JAWS SO WIDE THAT HE CAN SWALLOW A WHOLE TYRE?

12 WHICH FURRY, FOUR-LEGGED TRASHIE PATROLS THE COMPOUNDS OF TRASH TOWN LOOKING FOR LITTER FOR HIS COLLECTION?

13 WHICH THOUGHTLESS, NASTY CREATURES THROW THEIR RUBBISH ALL OVER TRASH TOWN?

14 WHICH MANGLED TRASHIE CAN WHIP YOU UP AN OOZY SMOOTHIE AT THE PRESS OF A FESTERING BUTTON?

15 WHICH SUPER PONGY, PLOPPY TRASHIE WAS BORN IN THE FILTHY SEWERS BELOW TRASH TOWN?

WHICH TRASHIE ARE YOU?

1 When you're hanging out with your putrid mates would you rather meet:
A) at the back of a manky old fridge?
B) down the back of a seat at the local cinema?
C) on a pile of steaming rubbish?
D) behind the bins?

2 Which foul feast would tempt you most?
A) the festering leftovers in a lunchbox?
B) a sticky, sickly snack, you just can't stop eating, even when you're fit to burst?
C) a pongy dog poo?
D) bottom of the bin?

3 What type of rank rubbish would you be:
A) festering food?
B) a trashy treat?
C) a critter with 6 or more legs?
D) a mangled up mutant?

If you were a Trashie, which Trashie would you be most like? Take this putrid test to find out the disgusting truth!

4 You'd most like to hang out with:
A) Kruddy Kebab and Sick Garlic
B) Burpy Slurpy and Rotty Pop
C) Rock Roach and Bad Ant
D) Bin Brute and Gas Ghost

5 A main feature of your gang is:
A) you're past your sell-by date
B) you're a star of Trash Town
C) you're creepy and slithery
D) you're ugly with multiple eyes and fungus fangs

MOSTLY A'S
YOU'RE A GROTESQUE GRUBZ.

MOSTLY B'S
YOU'RE A MANKY MOVIE TRASHIE.

MOSTLY C'S
YOU'RE A CREEPY, CRAWLY BIN-SECT.

MOSTLY D'S
YOU'RE A HIDEOUS, MUTANT BIN MONSTER.

WHO'S IN YOUR TRASH?

You've met the trash-tastic Trash Pack, so you know how putrid and smelly they are! How disgusting can you make your own creation? Use the space on the opposite page to draw your very own FOUL FRIEND, and then describe what they like doing, where they live and what they eat in the rubbish bin below.

CRUDDY COMIC

Now that you've created your own Trashie, use the spaces on these pages to draw your own cruddy comic story in which your putrid Trashie pal meets up with some of the Trash Pack for a TRULY ROTTEN ADVENTURE.

JOOSED'S JIGSAW JUMBLE

You know that sticky, oozy, gross goo in the bottom of your rubbish bin? Well that is the mangled-up Bin Monster, Joosed. TRASH-A-LICIOUS! Look at this vile puzzle and see if you can work out which sticky pieces fit in the gaps.

Answers

MUCKY MACARONI MESS-UP!

Eeeew! What's that oozing gunge? Ah, should've guessed – Spewster has just puked up his slimy meal all over the ground. If you dare, rummage amongst all this SPEWY MACARONI MESS and count up how many other foods are in the mucky pile.

Answer

What is that smell? Grab a peg for your nose and your most disgusting coloured pens to colour in these terrible Trashies. Act quickly, before they turn your stomach with their STINKY STENCH and have you reaching for the sick bucket!

The Trash Pack have been on a ROTTEN RUBBISH RAMPAGE! Look at this festering, fungusy scene for a few minutes. If you can bear it, try to remember all the gross garbage that you can see. Now turn the slimy page and see how good your putrid powers of observation are.

HOW MUCH RUBBISH CAN YOU REMEMBER?

WHAT CAN YOU REMEMBER? Answer these 8 questions to see if you were able to sift through all that terrible trash, without passing out from the SKUZZY STENCH!

1. How many flies are buzzing above the cab of the truck?

2. What colour is the sloppy slime pouring out of the back of the truck?

3. How many putrid Trashies are waiting outside the truck ready to rummage through all that rotting rubbish?

4. How many festering fish bones are there in the smelly scene?

5. Which cheesy Grubz Trashie is peeping out of the cab window?

6. How many half-eaten sandwiches have been thrown on the mud at the dump?

7. Which Trashie is squeezed in between Mouldy Milk and Smelly Onion?

8. What rubbery bit of old rubbish is lying on the mud in front of that sickly Grubz, Sticky Pop?

DISGUSTING DICE AND CRUDDY COUNTERS

Make the DISGUSTING DICE, cruddy counters, and revolting rubbish then use them to play the gross game of Trash Dash! on page 66.

YOU WILL NEED:
Glue stick and scissors

WHAT TO DO:

1. Ask an adult to help you carefully cut out the dice template, the 4 character counters and the 9 pieces of rubbish.

2. Fold the dice template along the dotted lines until it makes a cube.

3. Put glue on the tabs and stick them to the inside of the dice.

4. Your disgusting dice is now ready to use. Give it a roll!

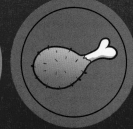

SEPTIX'S GROSS TOILET JOKES

Maybe this septic comedian's not ready for the stage yet 'cos some of his jokes REALLY STINK! Read this page and see what you think – will you be splitting your sides with laughter or reaching for the disinfectant...?

WHAT DO YOU CALL A KID WHO FILLS HIS NAPPY AT A BIRTHDAY CELEBRATION? PARTY POOPER!

WHAT DID ONE TOILET SAY TO THE OTHER? YOU LOOK FLUSHED!

WHY DID THE TOILET PAPER ROLL DOWN THE HILL? TO GET TO THE BOTTOM!

SOME CROOKS BROKE INTO THE POLICE STATION AND STOLE ALL OF THEIR TOILETS. THE POLICE ARE INVESTIGATING, BUT THEY HAVE NOTHING TO GO ON!

WHAT'S THE SMELLIEST SPORT? PING PONG!

THERE ARE TWO VERY GOOD REASONS NEVER TO DRINK TOILET WATER.... NUMBER ONE AND NUMBER TWO!

WHAT'S THE DIFFERENCE BETWEEN BROCCOLI AND BOGIES? KIDS WILL EAT BOGIES!

WHAT HAS FOUR WHEELS AND FLIES? A RUBBISH TRUCK!

TRASH DASH!

Word on the street is that the Junk Food Restaurant is giving a free burger, fries and milkshake to the first customer to fill up their rubbish bin with litter from the putrid Trash Town streets. Grab a rubbish bin and some friends, and race through town, picking up as much litter as you can to win. Hurry – but be careful you don't slip on some stinky slop on the way.

GOOD LUCK! LET'S HOPE YOU DON'T END UP WITH A SHAM-BURGER AND STENCH FRIES!

HOW TO PLAY:

- Turn to page 63 to make your dice, counters, and items of litter to play the game with.
- Place each item of litter on the game board circles with the matching number.
- Let the youngest player go first.
- Take turns throwing the dice and move along the streets of Trash Town, following the instructions as you go.
- If you land on a circle with litter on it, take that piece of litter for your trash can.
- The game ends when the first person reaches the Junk Food restaurant. All players must count the number of bits of litter in their trash cans.
- The winner is the one with the most pieces of litter.

19

20
You drop off your old newspapers at the Recycle Ranch. Great work! Take a piece of litter.

18

RECYCLE RANCH

17
You get into an argument with Feral Fridge at the Gizmo Graveyard. Go back 3 spaces.

THE TRASH PACK

16

COMPOST HEAP

SEWERAGE SKATEPARK

2
You step in dog poo. Miss a turn while you clean your shoes!

3

5

START HERE!

1

THE TRASH PACK

4

GRINDER

29
Alley Gator blocks your path. Run back 3 spaces before he sinks his jaws into you!

28

27

30 FINISH

Junk Food

26

WASTE WHARF

21

25
You outsmart Skabby Shark down at the Oozy Ocean. Move forward 2 spaces.

23
You slip on an old soggy banana skin. Go back 2 spaces.

22

24

15
You flag down a trash cart to take away a big pile of rubbish. Great job! Take any piece of litter.

14

13
You get overpowered by the terrible stench of Spewster. Miss a turn.

12

RADIATION CHAMBER

SEAGULL BEACH

6
You fall in the tar pit. Go back 2 spaces.

7

TAR PIT

9
You stop a litter bug dropping their litter. Well done! Move forward 3 spaces.

11

8

10

ANSWERS

P10 WASTED BANANA'S WORDSEARCH

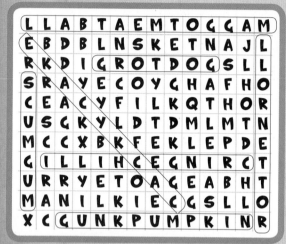

P11 SHOCKOLI'S SHADY SHADOWS

A-4, B-7, C-3, D-8, E-10, F-2, G-9, H-5, I-6, J-1

P14 TRASH-A-PILLAR'S CREEPY, CRAWLY CODE BREAKER

ACCORDING TO MY SCUMMY SOURCES, A DELIVERY OF FESTERING FOUL FOOD WILL BE ARRIVING ON A TRASH TRUCK. PUTRID PARADISE!

P15 SLUDGE SLUG'S MANKY MATHS

1) 12 2) 15 3) 3 4) 25%,
5) 1 LEFT OVER 6) 120

P18 GROTWEILER'S CRUDDY CROSSWORD

ACROSS 1) TOILET ROLL 4) BANANA SKIN 7) SARDINE CAN 8) SHOE 9) TYRE. DOWN 2) ROTTEN FISH 3) EGGS 4) BURGER 5) NAPPY 6) FALSE TEETH

P19 SKABBY SHARK'S AWFUL ANAGRAMS

1) SCABOON 2) PIGGY PIDGEON 3) NOXIOUS BEE 4) SLIME PYTHON 5) GARBAGE GOAT

P23 OILY OINTMENT'S ODD TRASHIE OUT

PICTURE C IS THE ODD ONE OUT

P30 SICKY, STINKY SEARCH AND FIND

P32 TRASHIE TRUE OR FALSE?

1) FALSE 2) TRUE 3) TRUE 4) FALSE 5) FALSE 6) TRUE 7) FALSE 8) TRUE 9) FALSE 10) FALSE

P33 SLIMY SPOT THE DIFFERENCE

P34 PUS POP'S PIMPLY PATHS PUZZLE

PATH A LEADS TO THE ICKY ICE CREAM!

P35 ROCK ROACH'S ROTTEN RIDDLES

RIDDLE 1: Bad Ant
RIDDLE 2: Ugly Bed Bug
RIDDLE 3: Feral Fly

P36 STINKY SUDOKU

P37 PUTRID POSTERS

P43 MESSY MAZE

P44 WASTE WORM'S WORDSEARCH

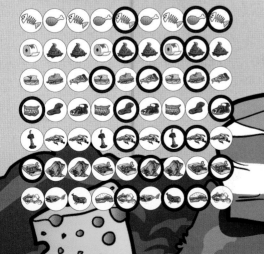

P45 PUTRID PATTERNS

P46 VUL-GORE'S WHO'S WHO?

A) JUNK MAIL B) LOCH MESS
C) BARF BBQ D) GIDDY SQUID

P47 KRUDDY KEBAB'S CRUSTY COUNTING

THERE ARE 14 CHICKEN LEGS.

P48-49 TRASH-TASTIC QUIZ

1) SICK GARLIC 2) SOUR SNAIL
3) GPS (GARBAGE PICK-UP SYSTEM)
4) CRUDDY KEBAB 5) JOOSED
6) BRAIN FREEZE 7) PIGGY PIGEON
8) YUCK KETCHUP 9) SEPTIX
10) WASTE WORM 11) SLIME PYTHON
12) GROTWEILER 13) LITTER BUGS
14) BROKEN BLENDER 15) POOP MONSTER

P56 JOOSED'S JIGSAW JUMBLE

1) D 2) E 3) B 4) A 5) C

P57 MUCKY MACARONI MESS-UP

THERE ARE 7 OTHER FOODS IN THE MACARONI

P62 HOW MUCH RUBBISH CAN YOU REMEMBER?

1) FOUR
2) PURPLE
3) SEVEN
4) THREE
5) PUTRID PIZZA
6) TWO
7) YUCK KETCHUP
8) AN OLD TYRE

PIGGY PIDGEON

SMELLY FISH

BAD-ANT

LOCH MESS

GARBAGE GOAT

TRASHOLA

STICKY POP

SLUDGE SLUG

BARF BBQ

UGLY BED BUG

BURPY SLURPY

SHOCKOLI